Quiz Wizard

Science &
Nature
Trivia

Marsha Kranes, Fred Worth & Steve Tamerius
Edited by Michael Driscoll

D0189810

POPULAR
GROUP

Popular Publishing Company, LLC
3 Park Avenue
New York, NY 10016

Cover art by Eileen Toohey

Cover and interior design by Tony Meisel

Manufactured in the United States of America

ISBN 1-59027-026-6

10 9 8 7 6 5 4 3 2 1

Questions

1. If man had a jumping ability proportional to that of the minuscule flea—which can make a horizontal leap of over a foot—how far would one leap take him?

2. When you cross cattle with buffalo, what do you get?

3. What is the most plentiful metal in the earth's crust?

4. An octopus has eight tentacles. How many does its relative the squid have?

5. What reason did Sigmund Freud give for sitting behind his patients' couch during psychoanalytic sessions?

6. How fast does lightning travel?

7. What is the normal body temperature of a horse?

8. What living creature is believed to enjoy more hours of daylight annually than any other?

9. What male mammal has the greatest number of mates in a season?

Answers

1. Five city blocks.

2. Beefalo.

3. Aluminum, most of which is extracted from bauxite.

4. Ten.

5. Freud wrote: "I cannot bear to be gazed at eight hours a day."

6. It travels 90,000 miles a second—almost half the speed of light (186,000 miles a second).

7. 100.5°F.

8. The Arctic tern, which travels twice a year from pole to pole—covering more than 20,000 miles round-trip—to enjoy nearly four months of continuous daylight during the Arctic summer and another four months during the Antarctic summer.

9. The northern fur seal, which averages 40 to 60 mates a season.

10. What gives the gemstone turquoise its distinctive color?

11. How fast do flying fish "fly"?

12. Who was the first to suggest using contact lenses to improve vision?

13. How many cubic feet of gas does a cow belch on an average day?

14. When lions and tigers mate, what do you call their cubs?

15. What are the seven colors of the rainbow?

16. How many times a minute does the average adult elephant's heart beat?

17. What animal always gives birth to identical quadruplets?

18. How much does the heart of the average man weigh?

19. How many sides are there to a snow crystal?

20. Why could we call William Stewart Halsted the "Mr. Clean" of medicine?

21. How many ribs does man have?

10. Traces of copper.

11. They average 35 mph and have been known to go as fast as 45 mph.

12. Leonardo da Vinci, in 1508.

13. Thirty-five.

14. Ligers when the father is a lion; tigons or tiglons when the father is a tiger.

15. Red, orange, yellow, green, blue, indigo and violet.

16. Only 25. In man, the average adult heartbeat is 70 to 80 times per minute.

17. The nine-banded armadillo, known as Dasypus novemcinctus—the only armadillo native to the U.S.

18. From 10 to 12 ounces. A woman's heart weighs from 8 to 10 ounces.

19. Six.

20. Halsted, developer of local anesthesia, was the first doctor to wear rubber gloves in surgery in 1890.

21. Twenty-four.

22. What Nobel Prize winner admitted that he had contributed his sperm to a sperm bank in hopes of producing exceptionally gifted children?

23. If seedless oranges don't have seeds, how are they propagated?

24. What vaccine caused more death and illness than the disease it was intended to prevent?

25. What distinction do the chevrotain (mouse deer) and dik-dik (antelope) share?

26. What is the hardest part of the normal human body?

27. What is the maximum lifespan of a goldfish in captivity?

28. What did Dr. Alfred Kinsey study before he turned his attention to our sexual behavior?

29. How many bee trips from flower to hive does it take to make a pound of honey?

30. A baby kangaroo is called a joey. What are its parents called?

31. What flower has more varieties than any other—at least 30,000—ranging in size from $^1/_4$ inch to 20 feet?

22. *William Shockley, inventor of the transistor.*

23. *By grafting. The original seedless orange was a mutant.*

24. *The swine flu vaccine, 1976.*

25. *They are among the world's tiniest-hoofed animals, reaching only 12 to 16 inches in height.*

26. *Tooth enamel.*

27. *Twenty-five years.*

28. *The gall wasp.*

29. *Forty thousand.*

30. *Mom's a flyer; Dad, a boomer.*

31. *The orchid.*

32. What famous American hero—educated as a mechanical engineer—helped design a germ-proof "artificial heart" in the early 1930s?

33. The mayfly lives six hours. How long do its eggs take to hatch?

34. A female black bear weighs about 300 pounds. How much does one of its babies weigh at birth?

35. What is the largest member of the dolphin family?

36. How many of the average adult's 32 permanent teeth are molars?

37. Approximately how many pounds of dung does the average elephant produce daily?

38. How were the first written messages transmitted by air?

39. How can you tell the age of a mountain goat?

40. What is the most plentiful element in seawater?

41. What device was introduced commercially in 1934 as a "portable superregenerative receiver and transmitter"?

42. What mammal has the world's shortest sperm?

43. What color is topaz in its pure state?

32. Charles Lindbergh, working with surgeon Alexis Carrel.

33. Three years.

34. One-half pound.

35. The killer whale.

36. 12. There are 3 per quadrant—top and bottom, on each side of the mouth.

37. 50.

38. By arrow—in the fifth century B.C., during the siege of Potidaea during the Peloponnesian War.

39. By the number of rings on its small, curved black horns. The first ring develops at age two, and another ring is added every spring thereafter. Both males and females grow horns.

40. Chlorine.

41. The walkie-talkie.

42. The hippopotamus.

43. It's colorless. Topaz takes on a variety of hues from trace elements, radiation and defects in its crystal structure. Pale gold-brown is its most common color.

44. Before the barometer was discovered, what animal did German meteorologists use to predict air pressure changes?

45. How many points must a stag elk have on each of its antlers to be considered mature?

46. The name of what dog breed, translated from German, means "monkey terrier"?

47. The giant panda is a member of the bear family. To what family does the much smaller red panda belong?

48. At what temperature does water boil at the top of Mount Everest?

49. What dog carries the name of the English minister who first bred it?

50. What is the most common transplant operation?

51. What did a National Aeronautics and Space Administration employee buy at a Wal-Mart in 1995 to protect the space shuttle from woodpeckers?

52. What is the largest rodent in North America?

53. Where did Leonardo da Vinci advise the adventurous to test his design for a rudimentary helicopter?

44. The frog. Frogs croak when the pressure drops.

45. Six. The antlers drop off at the end of each mating season and usually gain a point every time they grow back.

46. The Affenpinscher. In German, *affe* means "monkey" and *pinscher* means "terrier."

47. The raccoon family.

48. At 150℉ (or 70℃). At sea level, the boiling point of water is 212℉ (100℃). As you get higher, the atmospheric pressure drops, and with it the boiling point of water.

49. The Jack Russell. It's named for the Rev. John Russell.

50. The bone graft.

51. Six plastic owls.

52. The beaver. The porcupine is second.

53. Over a body of water. He wrote: "You will experiment with this instrument on a lake, so that in falling you will come to no harm."

54. What mammal can starve to death, despite a plentiful supply of food, if there are too many cool, cloudy days in a row?

55. At what standard level above ground—in feet—do meteorologists measure wind speed?

56. How many eyes does a bee have?

57. How much does a baby giraffe weigh at birth?

58. What planet has the greatest number of known satellites?

59. What is believed to be the largest of all the world's creatures with no backbone?

60. How many domestic silkworm cocoons does it take to make a man's tie?

61. What was the original purpose of ENIAC, the world's first "modern" computer?

62. What gives the mineral turquoise its distinctive color?

63. What creature was named walckvogel—"disgusting bird"—by the Dutch explorers who first spotted it in 1598?

64. What percentage of the average human brain is water?

54. The sloth, which has to sun itself daily to raise its body temperature so the bacteria in its stomach is warm enough to break down the leaves it eats. It often takes up to 100 hours to digest a stomachful of food.

55. 33 feet.

56. Five. The two large compound eyes on either side of its head are complex visual organs; the three ocelli (primitive eyes) on top of its head are believed to primarily detect light intensity.

57. About 150 pounds—and it's about 6 feet tall.

58. Saturn, with 20. Close behind are Jupiter, with 16, and Uranus, with 15.

59. The giant squid.

60. 110. It takes 630 to make a blouse.

61. To compute ballistic trajectories for artillery shells. ENIAC—an acronym for Electronic Numerical Integrator and Calculator—was introduced in 1946.

62. Traces of copper.

63. The flightless and now-extinct dodo. The Dutch saw it on the island of Mauritius.

64. 80 percent.

65. What does eccentricity mean to an astronomer?

66. What was the first human organ to be successfully transplanted?

67. What is alloyed with steel to make it stainless?

68. How long—in feet—is the trunk of the average full-grown elephant?

69. An average human has 46 chromosomes. How many does a cabbage have?

70. Which planet weighs over twice as much as all the other known planets combined?

71. How many inkblots are on the standard Rorschach test?

72. How many pounds of fish can a pelican hold in is pouch?

73. On an average day, how many hours does an elephant spend sleeping? How about a giraffe?

74. How fast—in miles per hour—do the fastest messages transmitted by the human nervous system travel?

75. Some armadillos give birth to duodecuplets. How many offspring is that?

76. What parts of the oleander plant are toxic?

65. *The degree to which an orbit deviates from a circle. The eccentricity of Earth's orbit is 0.017 (or 0.016722, to be more precise).*

66. *The kidney. Dr. Richard H. Lawler performed the transplant in 1956 in Chicago. His patient, Ruth Tucker, lived for five years with her new kidney.*

67. *Chromium.*

68. *8 feet.*

69. *18.*

70. *Jupiter, the largest planet in our solar system.*

71. *10.*

72. *About 25 pounds.*

73. *Four hours for both.*

74. *180 to 200 mph.*

75. *12.*

76. *All parts. The seeds of the ornamental bush are usually the most toxic, the leaves a little less and the flowers least—but still dangerous. Even the stems are toxic.*

77. On average, how many peas are there in a pod?

78. How many frames—or pictures—per second are transmitted over American television?

79. In years past what was used as transmission oil in Rolls-Royce automobiles?

80. What breed of dog is particularly distinctive because of a genetic condition called achondroplasia?

81. How many pointers were there on the first clocks with hands—made in the 14th century?

82. What temperature does the tungsten filament in an electric light reach when the light is turned on?

83. What bird has been spotted flying at 27,000 feet—higher than any other bird on record?

84. An estimated five million Americans suffer from a recurring ailment known as SAD. For what is SAD an acronym?

85. Why did German scientist Wilhelm Roentgen name the invisible rays he discovered X-rays?

86. How small is a pygmy right whale?

87. Who, long before Columbus, claimed the world was round, reasoning that if it were flat all the stars would be visible from all points on its surface?

77. Seven to nine.

78. 30.

79. Spermaceti oil—from the sperm whale.

80. The dachshund. Achondroplasia causes dwarfism—in the dachshund's case, abnormally short legs.

81. Only one—to tell the hour. Minute and second hands were added in the 16th and 17th centuries.

82. 2,577℃ (4,664℉).

83. The whooper swan. A flock of 30 was spotted by a pilot and picked up on radar at that altitude in 1967.

84. Seasonal affective disorder. It's a wintertime syndrome that can be treated with light.

85. Because he had no idea what the mysterious rays were.

86. It's about 16 feet long.

87. Aristotle, who offered as added proof the fact that the earth casts a spherical shadow on the moon during an eclipse.

88. When did American sales of cassette recordings surpass those of long-playing records?

89. What product was originally called the Soundabout when it was introduced in the U.S. in 1979?

90. The wild pomegranate is said to contain as many seeds as there are commandments in the Old Testament. How many is that?

91. What are zygodactyl feet?

92. What do the letters represent in the acronym DNA—the protein substance inside each cell that transmits genetic information from parent to child?

93. What is the larva of the ant lion called?

94. How long does a nanosecond last?

95. What animal is the source of the luxuriously soft wool known as cashmere?

96. What are the berries that grow on the hawthorn tree called?

97. What percentage of the world's food crops are pollinated by insects?

98. What is the difference between a crawfish and a crayfish?

88. *Eight years ago, in 1983.*

89. *The Sony Walkman. It was called the Stowaway in England.*

90. *613.*

91. *Feet with two toes pointing forward and two pointing backward—which birds such as parakeets, parrots and woodpeckers have.*

92. *Deoxyribonucleic acid.*

93. *A doodlebug.*

94. *One billionth of a second*

95. *The Kashmir goat, which lives in mountainous regions of Kashmir (in India), China and Iran.*

96. *Haws.*

97. *80 percent.*

98. *Nothing. Both names apply to the same freshwater crustacean.*

99. If you're selecting a three-course meal from a menu that offers four appetizers, seven entrées and three desserts, how many different meals can you order?

100. How many different chemical reactions occur in the normal human brain every second?

101. Which is larger, a crocodile's egg or a duck's egg?

102. In mathematics, what is the meaning of the term googol?

103. What word defines sounds too low for human hearing?

104. What reptile, according to ancient legend, was able to live in fire?

105. How many eyes do most spiders have?

106. Where are the grasshopper's "eardrums" located?

107. How did the bird known as the Baltimore oriole get its name?

108. How did the element strontium—also known by the symbol Sr and the atomic number 38—get its name?

99. 84 (that's 4 x 7 x 3).

100. At least 100,000.

101. They're about the same size—around three inches long.

102. It represents the number 1 followed by 100 zeroes—or 10100.

103. Infrasonic.

104. The salamander.

105. Eight.

106. Either on its forelegs or at the base of its abdomen, depending on the type of grasshopper.

107. From its colors, orange and black—the same as those on the heraldic coat of arms of the House of Baltimore, the family that founded the colony of Maryland and gave the city of Baltimore its name.

108. From Strontian, the Scottish mining village in which it was discovered.

109. What reply did newspaper tycoon William Randolph Hearst receive when he sent a telegram to a leading astronomer asking, "Is there life on Mars? Please cable one thousand words"?

110. How many miles of arteries, capillaries and veins are there in the adult human body?

111. What do beavers eat?

112. How many pounds of lunar rock and soil were collected and brought back to Earth from America's six expeditions to the moon?

113. What is the average lifespan of a human being's tastebud?

114. What planet is most like earth in size, mass, density and gravity?

115. Berkshire, Cheshire, Victoria and Poland China are breeds of what animal?

116. What percentage of its body weight does the average bear lose during hibernation?

117. What is the name of the computer program developed by the Los Angeles Police Department to help solve homicides?

118. In the original Hippocratic oath, by whom did the individual doctor swear to uphold the standards of professional behavior.

109. "Nobody knows"—repeated 500 times.

110. 62,000.

111. The bark of hardwood trees, leaves, and aquatic and shore plants. Beavers are vegetarians—and do not eat fish, as is widely believed.

112. 841.6.

113. From 7 to 10 days.

114. Venus.

115. The pig.

116. Up to 25 percent.

117. HITMAN—for Homicide Information Tracking Management Automation Network.

118. Apollo.

119. What do the bacteria Lactobacillus bulgaricus and Streptococcus thermophilus have in common?

120. What heavenly bodies have astronomers named after Brahms, Beethoven, Bach, the four Beatles and Eric Clapton—among others?

121. Where are seahorses hatched?

122. What animal is believed to limit its breeding to Macquarie Island, the rocky crest of a submerged South Pacific mountain?

123. How many pairs of legs does a shrimp have?

124. What is the difference between poultry and fowl?

125. The winter sleep of bears and other animals in cold climates is known as hibernation. What do we call the summer sleep of desert snails and other creatures in excessively warm or dry climates?

126. How many eyes—or eye spots—do most starfish have?

127. Fish travel in schools; what about whales?

128. How many muscles are there in an elephant's trunk?

129. How many beats per second does a bumblebee flap its wings?

119. Both must be present in a product for it to be labeled yogurt under U.S. Food and Drug Administration regulations.

120. Asteroids.

121. In a pouch on the male parent's belly. Eggs are deposited there by the female.

122. The royal penguin.

123. Five.

124. Poultry is domesticated fowl.

125. Estivation.

126. Five—one at the tip of each of its arms.

127. They get together in gams, or pods.

128. 100,000.

129. 160.

130. How long is a day on Mars?

131. What distance can the average healthy slug cover in a day?

132. Even with leap year, the average year is about 26 seconds longer than Earth's orbital period. How many years will it take for those seconds to build up into a single day?

133. How many watts are there in one horsepower of energy?

134. How many calories are consumed during an hour of typing?

135. What bird is the only one to have nostrils at the tip of its bill?

136. How many hairs does the average human scalp contain?

137. Which celebrated chemist-inventor is credited with developing plywood?

138. Do peacocks give birth to their young or do they lay eggs?

139. What is the only food a koala bear will eat?

140. What is cosmology?

130. 24 hours, 37 minutes and 22 seconds.

131. 50 yards. Slug races generally are held on a 1-yard course.

132. 3,323.

133. 746.

134. 110—just 30 more an hour than the number consumed while sleeping.

135. The kiwi.

136. Between 120,000 and 150,000.

137. Alfred Nobel, the inventor of dynamite and subsequent founder of the Nobel Prizes.

138. Neither—a peacock is male, but a peahen lays eggs.

139. The leaves of the eucalyptus tree.

140. The study of the origin and structure of the universe.

141. In the days when British sailors were given lime or lemon juice to prevent scurvy, what were Dutch sailors given?

142. How many milligrams of sodium are there in a teaspoon of salt?

143. How many bones are there in the human wrist?

144. To what plant family do the radish and turnip belong?

145. What part of the poison hemlock plant is deadly?

146. What are the colors of a primary rainbow, from inside to outside?

147. In the world of fruit, what is the rag?

148. What famous scientist was the first to figure out how to gauge the tidal effects of the moon and sun and how to calculate the exact path of a comet?

149. How many toes does a rhinoceros have on each foot?

150. What are the durian, cherimoya and mangosteen?

151. To what plant family do rosemary, oregano, thyme and marjoram belong?

141. Sauerkraut—or zourkool, as they called it.

142. Approximately 2,000.

143. Eight.

144. The mustard family.

145. All parts—the flowers, seeds, leaves, stem and roots.

146. Violet, indigo, blue, green, yellow, orange and red.

147. The white fibrous membrane inside the skin and around the sections of citrus fruit.

148. Sir Isaac Newton.

149. Three—encased in a hoof.

150. Exotic fruits.

151. The mint family.

152. A group of lions is a pride; a group of elephants, a herd; what is a group of leopards?

153. What poisonous weed gets it name from a historic American village?

154. What is a scalene triangle?

155. How many miles of nerves are there in the adult human body?

156. What diameter does a drop of liquid precipitation have to reach to graduate from drizzle to rain?

157. How fast do microwaves travel?

158. How many pints of air per minute does the average adult use during normal quiet breathing?

159. In mathematics, the symbol ∴ means therefore. What does á mean?

160. How much farther from Earth does the moon's orbit move every year?

161. What word was spelled out in the first neon sign?

162. By definition, what is the lifting capacity of one unit of horsepower?

152. A leap.

153. Jimson weed—which is a corruption of its original name, Jamestown weed, which was named for Jamestown, Virginia.

154. A triangle with unequal sides and angles.

155. 45.

156. It's a raindrop if it's over .02 inch in diameter.

157. 186,282 miles per second—the speed of light—as do all kinds of electromagnetic radiation including radio waves, infrared rays, visible light, ultraviolet light and X-rays.

158. Almost 13 pints, or 6 liters.

159. Because.

160. About 1.5 inches. Scientists believe the moon has been inching away from Earth for billions of years.

161. Neon. The small bright red sign was created by Dr. Perley G. Nutting, a government scientist, and exhibited at the 1904 Louisiana Purchase Exposition in St. Louis, Missouri—15 years before neon signs became widely used commercially.

162. The ability to raise 33,000 pounds one foot high in one minute.

163. What earthly creature has four "noses" and 3,000 tiny teeth?

164. A beehive produces between 100 and 200 pounds of honey a year. How much does a single worker honeybee manufacture in its lifetime?

165. How long does it take a whole fingernail to replace itself?

166. How fast per second does Earth travel in its orbit around the sun?

167. What is on the daily menu for an adult hippopotamus at the National Zoo in Washington, D.C.?

168. How many toes does an ostrich have?

169. What do you call the little bits of paper left over when holes are punched in data cards or tape?

170. What part of the human body is named for its resemblance to the sea horse?

171. How many eggs at a time do the most productive starfish release?

172. How fast does the sound of thunder travel per second?

173. How did the fish known as the guppy get its name?

163. The slug.

164. $^1/_2$ teaspoon.

165. About three months. Our nails grow about 0.1 mm (.004 inch) per day.

166. 18.5 miles per second.

167. About 10 pounds of kale, 3 gallons of high-protein cereal pellets and $^3/_4$ bale of alfalfa hay.

168. Four—two on each of its feet.

169. Chad.

170. The hippocampus—the ridge along each lateral ventricle of the brain. Hippocampus is Latin for "seahorse."

171. Up to 2.5 million.

172. About 1,100 feet.

173. From the man who discovered it and presented specimens to the British Museum—naturalist R.J.L. Guppy of Trinidad.

174. How many meteorites hit the earth each year?

175. How often does the epidermis, the outer layer of our skin, replace itself?

176. Modern computer chips consist of millions of transistors. How many transistors were on the first chips made in 1958?

177. In 1988 what did a panel of 10 international design experts pick as the best-designed product costing less than $5?

178. In computerese, what does wysiwyg mean?

179. Before surgical dressings of gauze and cotton were introduced, what was commonly used to cover wounds in American hospitals?

180. How did the magnolia get its name?

181. To what plant family does the asparagus belong?

182. What is a group of rhinoceroses called?

183. What is the only member of the cat family that does not have retractable claws?

184. Noble Prize-winning missionary Dr. Albert Schweitzer had a pet named Parsifal. What kind of animal was it?

174. *About 500—most of them go unrecorded, falling into oceans, deserts and other uninhabited areas.*

175. *About once every four weeks.*

176. *Just two.*

177. *The eightpenny finishing nail.*

178. *It's shorthand for what you see is what you get.*

179. *Pressed sawdust.*

180. *From French botanist Pierre Magnol, who introduced it.*

181. *It's a member of the lily family—as are the onion and garlic.*

182. *A crash.*

183. *The cheetah.*

184. *A pelican.*

185. There are an estimated 10 trillion stars in our galaxy, the Milky Way. How many are visible to the naked eye from the earth?

186. What is a geoduck?

187. How can you tell the sex of a horse by its teeth?

188. What animal is believed to have the best hearing?

189. From what language do we get the two scientific terms used to describe hardened lava fields: aa and pahoehoe?

190. What was the first human organ to be successfully transplanted?

191. How many pounds per day does a baby blue whale gain during its first seven months of life?

192. What is the "lead" in a lead pencil?

193. Why is the small shorebird Americans know as the red phalarope called the grey phalarope in England?

194. By what popular name do we know the fluorine-based compound polytetrafluoro-ethylene, or PTFE?

195. How many toes does a giraffe have on each foot?

185. *About 6,000.*

186. *A large clam.*

187. *Most males have 40 teeth; most females 36.*

188. *The barn owl—even though its ears can't be seen. Its face is dish-shaped, enabling the owl to receive sounds like sonar.*

189. *Hawaiian. Aa is lava that is rough and jumbled; pahoehoe is lava that is smooth and wavy.*

190. *The kidney. Dr. Richard H. Lawler performed the transplant in 1956 in Chicago. His patient, Ruth Tucker, lived for five years with her new kidney.*

191. *At least 200 pounds. A baby blue whale—which is about 22 feet long at birth—grows 29 feet longer in its first seven months.*

192. *Graphite and clay. Lead pencils never contained lead—but graphite was originally thought to be a type of lead.*

193. *The bird is named for its summer plumage in America; for its winter plumage in England.*

194. *Teflon.*

195. *Two.*

196. Where are a butterfly's tastebuds located?

197. What popular dog was originally known as a waterside terrier?

198. How long is the tongue of the giant anteater of South America?

199. What is a horse called before it reaches age one and becomes a yearling?

200. How long is the average adult's spinal cord?

201. What bacterium is named for German pediatrician Theodor Escherich?

202. What six elements make up over 95 percent of all living material?

203. If a carnivore is a meat-eating animal, what's a frugivore?

204. At what wind speed does a snowstorm become a blizzard?

205. What part of a horse's anatomy is known as a stifle?

196. On its legs. They are microscopic hairs, called sensilla, on the terminal part of the butterfly's legs.

197. The airdale. It was renamed when a judge at the Airdale Agriculture Society Show in Bingley, Yorkshire— in the valley of the Aire River—suggested another name be found for the locally bred dog.

198. 22 to 24 inches. It uses its tongue to lap up ants— about 35,000 a day.

199. A weanling. It remains a weanling until its first birthday, which is always on January 1.

200. From 17 to 18 inches. Its weight, minus membranes and nerves, is about 1 $\frac{1}{2}$ ounces.

201. E. coli. The E is for Escherichia, after its discoverer, who first identified the bacteria in 1885 and called it Bacterium coli commune. It was give its current name in 1919.

202. Carbon, hydrogen, nitrogen, oxygen, phosphorus and sulfur.

203. A fruit eater.

204. In excess of 35 miles an hour.

205. The joint on the hind leg—between the femur and the tibia—that corresponds anatomically to a human's knee. It's also know as the stifle joint.

206. Which is the largest order of mammals, with about 1,700 species?

207. How many vertebrae does a human being have?

208. What is the body's largest organ—by weight?

209. In the world of horses, what's a palomilla?

210. What are the only two types of mammals that are poisonous?

211. How many seeds from the giant sequoia tree—the most massive of all living things—are there in an ounce?

212. Which is the longest muscle in the human body?

213. How many mosquito-size insects is the one-ounce brown bat—the most common bat in North America—capable of eating in an hour of nighttime dining?

214. What form of precipitation generally falls only from cumulonimbus clouds?

215. What part of the body is the Brannock device used to measure?

216. How wide an angle is the average person's field of vision?

206. Rodents. Bats are second, with about 950 species.

207. 33—7 cervical, 12 thoracic (or dorsal), 5 lumbar, 5 sacral, and 4 caudal (or coccygeal).

208. The lungs. Together they weigh about 42 ounces. The right lung is two ounces heavier than the left, and the male's lungs are heavier than the female's.

209. A milk-white horse with white mane and tail.

210. Shrews and platypuses. Some shrews have slightly poisonous bites, and male platypuses have poisonous spurs on their hind legs.

211. 8,000. The seeds are $1/_4$ inch long. The largest giant sequoia in existence, the General Sherman, is in California's Sequoia National Park.

212. The sartorius, which runs from the pelvis across the front of the thigh to the top of the tibia below the knee.

213. About 500.

214. Hail. Cumulonimbus clouds are heavy, swelling, vertically developed clouds.

215. The foot. It's the device used in shoe stores to determine your shoe size.

216. About 200 degrees.

217. In what country did the French poodle originate?

218. What mammal has the heaviest brain?

219. What is your buccal cavity?

220. How fast—in miles per hour—can a crocodile move on land? How about in water?

221. How many times brighter is a full moon than a half moon?

222. What does a mellivorous bird eat?

223. With the exception of the whale, what animal has the largest mouth?

224. How much does the skeleton of the average 160-pound body weigh?

225. Pine wood ignites at 800°F. At what temperature does charcoal ignite?

226. What creature produces sperm that are 2/3 inch long—the longest in the world?

227. What planet's moon is the largest satellite in our solar system?

228. How did scientist Louis Pasteur make sure the food he was served at the homes of his friends was safe to eat?

217. In Germany, where it was known as the pudel, from a word meaning "to splash in the water." In France, it's known as the caniche, which is derived from "duck dog." Its Latin name is *canis familiaris aquatius*.

218. The sperm whale. Its brain weighs up to 20 pounds—six times heavier than a human's.

219. The inside of your mouth.

220. On land, up to 30 mph; in water, 20.

221. 10 times.

222. Honey. Mell- comes from a Greek word for "honey."

223. The hippopotamus.

224. About 29 pounds.

225. 580°F.

226. Some fruit flies of the genus Drosophila. Their sperm, more than 300 times longer than human sperm, are six times longer than the fly itself—but hair-thin and all balled up.

227. Jupiter's moon Ganymede.

228. He checked it with a portable microscope he carried with him.

229. Where in the human body is the only bone that is not connected to another bone?

230. How can you tell a fish's age?

231. What is the first bird mentioned in the Bible?

232. What animal's skin is the source of true moroccan leather?

233. How did the skeleton of the more-than-three-million-year-old female hominid discovered in Ethiopia in 1974 come to be called Lucy?

234. What unpopular bird's Latin name is Sturnus vulgaris?

235. What mammal is the only living member of its order?

236. What two types of dogs were crossed to create the whippet?

237. What is the only land mammal native to New Zealand.

229. In the throat, at the back of the tongue. It's the horseshoe-shaped hyoid bone, which supports the tongue and its muscles. Also known as the lingual bone, it is suspended by ligaments from the base of the skull.

230. From the number of growth rings on each of its scales. Each pair of rings represents a year—the dark narrow rings represent winter; the wider, lighter rings represent summer.

231. The raven. It appears in Genesis 8:7, when it is sent out from the ark by Noah to see if the flood waters have abated.

232. The goat.

233. Donald Johanson, the anthropologist who found the skeleton, and his colleagues were listening to the Beatles' song "Lucy in the Sky with Diamonds" while they were discussing and celebrating the discovery—and they started referring to the skeleton by that name.

234. The common, or European, starling, which is held in low esteem by bird-watchers because it takes the nest of domestic songbirds, and by farmers because it often damages fruit and grain crops.

235. The aardvark. Its order is Tubulidentata.

236. The greyhound and the terrier.

237. The bat.

238. How fast can a sailfish swim—in miles per hour?

239. What is the main food of mosquitoes?

240. What wind speed does a storm have to exceed to be given a name by the National Hurricane Center?

241. What plant's name—derived from the French—means "lion's tooth"?

242. How many times per second does a mosquito beat its wings?

243. What is the only female deer to grow antlers?

244. What physical symptom is exhibited by those who suffer from blepharospasms?

245. What does the Chemical symbol Fe_2O_3 represent?

246. A female pig is called a sow; what is a male pig called?

247. How many legs does a spider have?

248. How many true vocal cords does a normal person have?

249. What is the wrinkled flesh that hangs from the neck of a turkey called?

238. More than 60 mph, faster than any other known fish. Humans have been recorded swimming up to 5.19 mph.

239. Nectar from flowers, not your blood. The blood we lose to mosquitoes—females only—is needed for protein to help them lay their eggs.

240. 39 mph.

241. The dandelion. In French it's called *dente de lion*, for the toothlike points on its leaves.

242. Up to 600.

243. The reindeer.

244. Uncontrollable winking.

245. Rust.

246. A boar. A baby is a piglet.

247. Eight—four pairs, which is one of the features that distinguishes a spider from an insect, which has three pairs of legs.

248. Two. They are called true (or inferior) vocal cords and are involved in the production of sound. We also have a pair of false (or superior) vocal cords that have no direct role in producing the voice.

249. The wattle.

250. If the angles of a pentagon are equal, what are they—in degrees?

251. Where in the world are you most likely to find lemurs in the wild?

252. Where on the human face is there a muscle known as the corrugator?

253. Before the advent of electricity, how did theatrical companies put their stars in the spotlight?

254. What was the "dephlogisticated air" discovered by English scientist Joseph Priestley in 1774?

255. What is the average minimum speed in miles per hour needed for a bird to remain aloft?

256. What planet has surface winds that have been measured at 1,500 mph—the strongest in the solar system?

257. How many of an adult domestic cat's 30 teeth are canines?

258. How much coal does it take to get the same amount of energy provided by burning one full cord of seasoned firewood?

259. How tall is a baby giraffe at birth?

260. How are all the workers of an African driver ant colony, numbering around 22 million, related?

250. 108 degrees. Such a pentagon is called a regular pentagon.

251. In Madagascar.

252. On the forehead. It's the muscle that contracts the forehead into wrinkles and pulls the eyebrows together.

253. Lime was burned in a lamp, creating an intense white light that was directed at featured performers—and giving us the word limelight.

254. Oxygen. At the time phlogiston was believed to be a chemical released during combustion.

255. 11 mph—or 16 $\frac{1}{2}$ feet per second.

256. Neptune.

257. 4. The cat also has 12 incisors, 10 premolars and 4 molars.

258. One ton.

259. About 6 feet.

260. They're all sisters—although they have different fathers.

261. On what planet is the largest known mountain in the solar system?

262. How fast can an ostrich run?

263. How was the Tonkinese breed of cat developed?

264. What animal's name means "earth pig"?

265. If you hear thunder 10 seconds after you see lightning, how far away was the lightning?

266. What was Sigmund Freud's fee—in U.S. dollars—for one session of psychoanalysis in 1925?

267. How many bones are there in the human skull?

268. How much does an adult giraffe's heart weigh?

269. How many newborn opossums can fit in a teaspoon?

270. How many constellations are there?

271. The name of what flower means "fleshlike"?

261. On Mars. Called Olympus Mons, it's a volcano more than three times the height of Mount Everest.

262. About 40 miles per hour—taking strides of 12 to 15 feet.

263. By crossing a Burmese with a Siamese.

264. The aardvark's—in the Afrikaans language.

265. 2 miles away. Sound travels about a mile in 5 seconds.

266. $25—adjusted for inflation, that would be about $160 today.

267. 29—the cranium has 8; the face, 15 (including the lower jaw); the ears, 6.

268. About 25 pounds. It's 2 feet long, with walls up to 3 inches thick. It has quite a job pumping blood to the brain—which is sometimes 12 feet above the heart.

269. About 24. They're very small—about .07 ounce each—at birth.

270. 100,000

271. The carnation, which was named for a rosy pink color developed by artists during the 16th century. The first carnations were that color. In Latin, carnis means "flesh."

272. What part of the human body is the axilla?

273. What is a diadromous fish?

274. How many sweat glands are there on the skin of the average adult human being?

275. How many toes does a pig have on each of its feet?

276. The average adult takes 14 breaths a minute; how many does an infant take?

277. How much horsepower does the typical horse provide?

278. How fast can a swordfish swim?

279. What animal has the largest eyes—each a foot or more in diameter?

280. What contribution did Sarah Nelmes make to medicine in 1796?

281. What are the odds of having an ear of corn with an odd number of rows of kernels?

282. What is the gestation period for an elephant?

272. The armpit.

273. A fish—such as salmon or sturgeon—that can exist in both salt water and fresh water.

274. More than 2 million—an estimated 2,381,248, according to *Gray's Anatomy*.

275. Four—two of which touch the ground.

276. 33.

277. About 24. Horsepower is the power needed to lift 33,000 pounds 1 foot in 1 minute. Scientists came up with the 24 horsepower figure based on a horse weighing about 1,320 pounds.

278. More than 60 miles an hour. It and the sailfish are the fastest swimming fish.

279. The giant squid. The largest creature without a backbone, it weighs up to 2.5 tons and grows up to 55 feet long.

280. Edward Jenner used her cowpox lesions for the first smallpox vaccination.

281. Zero. There are always an even number of rows.

282. From 20 to 22 months. Baby weighs in at about 200 pounds.

283. What is the largest deer in the world?

284. From where in nature do we get quinine, the medicine used to treat and prevent malaria?

285. How much syrup does the average sugar maple tree yield each season?

286. What animal, traveling at an average ground speed of six to eight feet per minute, is the slowest moving land mammal?

287. In Space Age lingo, what is LOX?

288. Which has more cervical vertebrae—a mouse, a man or a giraffe?

289. How many average-size houses can you make from one giant sequoia—the biggest living thing on earth today?

290. What bird strays as far as 2,500 miles from its nest to find food for its young?

291. How old is the average 1 $\frac{1}{2}$-pound lobster?

292. What is the lightest substance known to science?

293. What makes flamingos pink?

283. *The Alaska bull moose, which has been known to reach a shoulder height of 7 ¹/₂ feet and a weight of up to 1,800 pounds.*

284. *From the bark of the cinchona tree, a South American evergreen.*

285. *One to one and a quarter quarts.*

286. *The three-toed sloth, which spends 18 hours of every day sleeping.*

287. *Liquid oxygen, a component of rocket fuel.*

288. *All have the same number, seven.*

289. *Fifty. The sequoia often exceeds 300 feet in height and 25 feet in diameter. Its seed weighs only 1/6000 ounce.*

290. *The albatross, which has the largest wingspan of any living bird—over 11 feet.*

291. *About 8 years old. If it avoids the lobster trap, it can live to about 50 and weigh up to 35 pounds.*

292. *The element hydrogen, with a specific gravity of 0.0695 compared to air. Helium is the second lightest with a specific gravity of 0.139.*

293. *Canthaxantin, a Vitamin A-like chemical found in the soda lakes where they feed. Away from the lakes, flamingos turn white.*

294. How many muscles does a caterpillar have?

295. The swallows traditionally return to San Juan Capistrano, California, on March 19. What birds return to Hinckley, Ohio, four days earlier?

296. How did a Nebraska mule named Krause make news, first in 1984 and again in 1985?

297. How many times a day does the average human heart beat?

298. How many bones does the average human adult have?

299. How many muscles do we use when we smile broadly?

300. You get a geep when you cross what two animals?

301. What is the world's tallest grass, which sometimes grows 130 feet or more?

302. What is the only pouched animal found in North America—and the only one not found in Australia?

303. In what direction do most cyclones whirl?

304. What is the ermine known as during its off-seasons, when its fur isn't white?

305. How many leaves does the average mature oak tree shed in the fall?

294. *Four thousand—more than five times as many as a human?*

295. *The turkey buzzards.*

296. *Although mules are almost always infertile, Krause gave birth to baby mules in both years. Each birth was a billion-to-one shot.*

297. *About 100,000—to pump five quarts of blood every minute.*

298. *Two hundred and six.*

299. *Seventeen.*

300. *A sheep and a goat. Some prefer to call it a shoat.*

301. *Bamboo.*

302. *The opossum.*

303. *Clockwise in the Southern Hemisphere; counterclockwise in the Northern Hemisphere.*

304. *The short-tailed weasel, also known as a stoat.*

305. *About 700,000.*

306. What part of the human body is called the atlas?

307. Who was the first person known to have died of radiation poisoning?

308. What is the only breed of dog to have a black, rather than pink, tongue?

309. What expensive fur do we get from an aquatic cat-sized rodent with orange teeth called the coypu?

310. What element is named after a state?

311. How long does it take light from the sun to travel to earth, a distance of about 93,000,000 miles?

312. What part of the human body has the thinnest skin?

313. Which is the only bird that can fly backward?

314. An animal named Louise has helped West German police sniff out narcotics, explosives and other contraband. What kind of animal is she?

315. What temperature do honey bees maintain in their hives year-round?

316. How many bones are there in your big toe?

317. What are the only two mammals that lay eggs rather than give birth to live offspring?

306. The first vertebra of the neck, which holds up your head—just as Atlas held up the world.

307. Two-time Nobel Prize-winner Marie Curie.

308. The chow.

309. Nutria.

310. Californium, first produced in 1950 by scientists at the University of California at Berkeley.

311. About eight minutes.

312. The eyelid—it's less than 1/500 inch thick.

313. The tiny hummingbird.

314. A wild boar.

315. An even 94°F.

316. Fourteen, the same as in your other toes.

317. The duck-billed platypus and the spiny anteater.

318. How many teeth are there in our first set of teeth—our baby teeth?

319. What important point did Scottish mathematician John Napier come up with in the early seventeenth century?

320. What was the name of the first computer used for weather research?

321. When is Halley's comet, first observed in 240 B.C. and last seen in 1986, expected to appear again?

322. How much does the blue whale, the world's largest mammal, weigh at birth?

323. For what operation was Antonio de Egas Moniz of Portugal awarded the Nobel Prize in medicine in 1949?

324. How tall is a newborn giraffe?

325. Do identical twins have identical fingerprints?

326. What bird has the longest nestling life—taking up to nine months to fly?

327. In geology, what is calving?

328. What common chemical compound is represented by the formula NH_3?

329. In the animal kingdom, what is a glutton?

318. Twenty. Our second set has 32.

319. The decimal point.

320. MANIAC—an acronym for Mathematical Analyzer, Numerical Integrator and Computer.

321. In the year 2061.

322. Two tons. Fully grown, it will weigh as much as 150 tons.

323. The now-discredited prefrontal lobotomy.

324. Five and a half feet, head to hoof.

325. No. No two sets of prints are alike, including those of identical twins.

326. The wandering albatross.

327. The breaking off or detachment of an iceberg from a glacier that has reached the sea, or the separation of a portion of a floating iceberg.

328. Ammonia.

329. A wolverine.

330. How did the tarantula get its name?

331. What is the name of the protein—the most abundant in the human body—that holds our skin together?

332. How much saliva does the average human produce daily?

333. How long are the antlers of the pudu, the smallest deer in the world?

334. How many muscles are there in the human ear?

335. What kind of creature do Australians call the tasseled wobbegong?

336. How many teeth does a turtle have?

337. What color are the eggs laid by the flightless emu, the largest bird alive today after the ostrich?

338. What is the world's largest living fish?

339. How many calories do hibernating bears burn daily?

340. What is the average lifespan of a red blood cell in the normal human body?

341. How many bones are there in the human hand?

330. From the Italian seaport city of Taranto, where the hairy, venomous wolf spider once abounded.

331. Collagen.

332. One quart.

333. They grow to 3 inches long. The pudu, found in northwest and southwest South America, is about 14 inches tall to the shoulders and weighs about 20 pounds.

334. Six.

335. A shark found near Australia's Great Barrier Reef.

336. None—turtles are toothless, although some have sharp, jagged edges on their horny jaws that function as teeth.

337. Green.

338. The harmless whale shark, which reaches up to 50 or more feet in length and weighs up to 20 tons.

339. About 4,000.

340. Four months.

341. 27.

342. What is N_2O—nitrous oxide—more commonly called?

343. In what order do most pigs move their legs when walking normally?

344. How many miles of blood vessels are there in the average human body?

345. What is the softest mineral known?

346. What is the largest living invertebrate?

347. What color is the blood of an octopus?

348. What is unique about the food-catching technique of the anhinga—also known as the snakebird, darter or water turkey?

349. What were the first objects in the solar system discovered by means of a telescope?

350. How many teeth does a normal adult dog have?

351. How long is a Martian year in Earth days—a year being the length of time it takes the planet to revolve once around the Sun?

352. How did the quarter horse get its name?

353. What animal has more teeth than any other North American land mammal?

342. Laughing gas.

343. Left front foot first, then right rear foot, right front foot, left rear foot.

344. About 62,000.

345. Talc.

346. The giant squid, which achieves a length of more than 60 feet—tentacles included.

347. Pale bluish-green.

348. It spears fish with its long, straight, sharp bill—the only bird to do so. It has extra cervical vertebrae, which enable it to coil its neck and then release it with viper-like speed.

349. The four largest satellites of Jupiter—Ganymede, Io, Callisto and Europa.

350. 42—that's 20 on the upper jaw and 22 on the lower jaw. The adult human has 32, evenly divided between upper and lower jaws.

351. 687 days.

352. From its speed in running the quarter mile.

353. The opossum, the only marsupial native to North America. It has 50 teeth.

354. What two elements comprise almost 100 percent of the matter in the universe?

355. In the American system of mathematical progressions, what five denominations come after million, billion and trillion?

356. In costume jewelry, when gold is electroplated to metal, how thick must the layer of gold be?

357. What is present in the variety of quartz stone known as cat's-eye that gives it its unique glowing appearance?

358. In what direction does the jet stream flow?

359. What is the most abundant metallic element in the earth's surface?

360. What are the ornamental plumes of the male egret called?

361. If you traveled at a snail's pace, how much ground would you cover in an hour?

362. How many fat cells does the average adult have?

363. Where are the pyramids of Malpighi and the pyramids of Ferrein?

364. Bovine means cow-like. What does murine mean?

354. Hydrogen (approximately 75 percent) and helium (approximately 25 percent). The remaining, heavier elements constitute a mere fraction of existence.

355. Quadrillion, quintillion, sextillion, septillion and octillion.

356. At least seven millionths of an inch thick—and the gold must be at least 10-karat.

357. Asbestos fibers. The glow is known as chatoyancy.

358. From west to east.

359. Aluminum—it accounts for an estimated 8 percent of the solid portion of the earth's crust.

360. Aigrettes.

361. 25 feet—for a great many species.

362. Between 40 and 50 billion.

363. In the human body—in the kidneys.

364. Mouse-like.

365. What is a group of foxes called?

366. A cob is a male swan; a cygnet is a baby. What is the female called?

367. What is a female rabbit called?

368. How did the horse chestnut tree get its name?

369. What tree's name contains all five vowels?

370. What are amberjack, cusk and pout?

371. What are Shaggy Mane, Slimy Gomphidius, Inky Cap, Sulphur Top and Pig's Ears?

372. What is the skin that peels off after a bad sunburn?

373. What word best describes the snout of a pig?

374. What is a group of owls called?

375. What are baby beavers called?

376. What is a perfusionist's role in a hospital operating room?

377. There are two atria in the human body—where are they?

367. A skulk.

366. A pen.

367. A doe. A male is a buck; a baby, a kit or kitten. The act of giving birth is known as kindling.

368. From the early use of its chestnuts as a medicine for horses.

369. The sequoia's.

370. Fish.

371. Mushrooms.

372. Blype.

373. Gruntle.

374. A parliament.

375. Kits or kittens.

376. Running the heart-lung machine during open-heart surgery. The machine keeps the patient's heart pumping while it removes carbon dioxide from the blood and adds oxygen to it.

377. In the heart. They are the two upper chambers (auricles) that receive the blood from the veins and pump it into the two lower chambers (ventricles).

378. What do the letters CAT represent in CAT scan—the three-dimensional composite image that can be taken of body, brain or lungs?

379. What belief was Galileo forced to recant by the Inquisition in 1633?

380. In astronomy, what is a white dwarf?

381. Wild turkeys can run at speeds of at least 12 miles an hour. How fast can they fly?

382. What does the acronym DSB mean to a hospital worker?

383. What famous naturalist penned a book entitled, The Formation of Vegetable Mold, Through the Action of Worms, With Observations on Their Habits?

384. What was the Calypso, Jacques-Yves Cousteau's ship, before he converted it into an oceanographic research vessel?

385. Who was the first person to record that the number of rings in the cross section of a tree trunk reveals its age?

386. What is the meaning of the word "lore" when it's used by an ornithologist?

387. What's a winkle?

378. Computerized axial tomography.

379. That the earth revolved around a stationary sun. He was kept under house arrest for the last eight years of his life for debunking the traditional belief that the earth was the center of the universe.

380. The dense, burned-out remains of a star; a stellar corpse.

381. Up to 55 miles an hour.

382. Drug-seeking behavior. The designation is used for a patient or wannabe patient who is complaining of a bogus ailment in an attempt to get narcotics.

383. Charles Darwin, who is better known for his revolutionary tome, Origin of the Species. His book on worms, a pioneering work in the field of quantitative ecology published in 1881, was his last.

384. A minesweeper.

385. Leonardo da Vinci. He also discovered that the width between the rings indicates annual moisture.

386. The space between a bird's eye and its bill.

387. An edible sea snail.

388. In the world of living things, what are zebus? How about zebubs?

389. What celestial body got its name from a Greek word meaning "long-haired"?

390. How many compartments does a normal cow's stomach have?

391. The discovery of what semiprecious stone often indicates that diamonds are nearby?

392. To what animal family does the wolverine belong—as its largest member?

393. Why are Mercury and Venus known as inferior planets?

394. How much silver must an item contain to be considered sterling?

395. What system of healing did Canadian-born grocer Daniel David Palmer formally introduce in Davenport, Iowa, in September 1895?

396. What part of a horse is the pastern?

397. What is unusual about the tail of the flightless kiwi bird?

388. Zebus are humped cattle found in India, China and northern Africa; zebubs are tsetse-like flies found in Ethiopia.

389. Comet. The name comes from the Greek komëtës, an adjective formed from the verb koman, "to wear long hair."

390. Four. The rumen, reticulum (storage area), omasum (where water is absorbed), and abomasum (the only compartment with digestive juices).

391. Garnet.

392. The weasel family, Mustelidae.

393. Their orbits are closer to the sun than Earth's orbit. Planets orbiting the sun beyond Earth are referred to as superior planets.

394. 92.5 percent.

395. Chiropractic medicine. Although new at the time, the principles upon which chiropractic medicine was based can be traced back to the earliest physicians—including Hippocrates (460–370 B.C.). Palmer created the name "chiropractic" by combining the Greek words for hand, cheir, and practical (or efficient), praktikos.

396. The part of the foot between the fetlock and the hoof.

397. It doesn't exist. The kiwi has no tail feathers.

398. What is silviculture?

399. How many times its own body weight can a worker ant carry?

400. In Web site addresses on the Internet, what does http stand for?

401. How many degrees can a great horned owl turn its head?

402. According to Raymond Loewy, the industrial designer who introduced streamlining to packaging, what are the two most perfectly designed containers ever made?

403. What essential piece of office equipment did Johann Vaaler invent in 1900?

404. What Scottish innkeeper's son invented the thermos bottle in 1892?

405. Who started the first airship passenger service in 1910?

406. Who invented the aerosol valve in 1949?

407. Who invented the Johnny Mop, the disposable toilet bowl cleaner on a stick?

408. What did Englishman Edwin Budding invent in 1830?

398. Forestry—the planting of trees for the preservation of forests. The Latin word *silva* means "forest."

399. Up to 50 times its weight. Worker ants are always female.

400. Hypertext transfer protocol.

401. 270 degrees.

402. The old Coca-Cola bottle and the egg.

403. The paper clip.

404. Sir James Dewar, who later invented cordite, the first smokeless explosive.

405. Ferdinand, Graf von Zeppelin, who flew passengers 300 miles between Düsseldorf and Friedrichshafen.

406. Richard Nixon's buddy Robert Abplanalp.

407. Dorothy Rodgers, wife of composer Richard Rodgers.

408. The lawn mower, or as he described it: "machinery for the purpose of cropping or shearing the vegetable surface of lawns."

409. On what wardrobe item did zipper inventor Whitcomb Judson use his first "clasp locker" in the late nineteenth century?

410. Who invented charcoal briquettes?

411. With what product did the term "brand name" originate?

412. What do the initials S.O.S. stand for in the brand of steel-wool soap pads marketed under that name?

413. A certain Capt. Hanson Gregory is credited with a curious invention: It has neither weight nor density; it can be seen but not felt. What is it?

414. What piece of modern office equipment was first developed in 1842 by Scottish clockmaker Alexander Bain?

415. Where did Robert Fulton launch his first steamboat?

416. Who is second only to Thomas Edison in the number of U.S. patents granted for inventions?

417. What state was the home of the U.S. auto industry before World War I and the rise of Michigan?

409. A pair of boots.

410. Henry Ford, to make use of scrap wood left over in the manufacture of the Model T.

411. Whiskey. Producers branded their names on the barrels they shipped out.

412. Save Our Saucepans.

413. The doughnut hole.

414. The facsimile machine—better known as the fax. Bain was granted a patent in 1843 for his electro-chemical duplicating telegraph system, which was capable of transmitting crude images short distances.

415. In Paris, on the Seine, in 1803. It sank. But Fulton made history four years later when his steamboat Clermont traveled the Hudson River from New York City to Albany.

416. Edwin Land, inventor of the Polaroid camera.

417. Indiana, where there were once hundreds of automakers. The last, Studebaker, shut down its operations in 1963. The Indianapolis 500 auto race, held annually on Memorial Day weekend, dates back to 1911, when Indianapolis was an auto-manufacturing center.

418. How much did the first three minutes of a call cost when commercial telephone service was introduced between New York and London in 1927?

419. What was Henry Ford's first mass-produced car?

420. Who invented the coffee filter?

421. What were the first products marketed in aerosol containers?

422. What toy did American author John Dos Passos invent and have patented in 1959?

423. What was produced when sewing machines were first set up in a French factory in 1841?

424. How often did the spark plugs in the Model T Ford have to be cleaned—in miles driven?

425. Who invented the first hideaway bed ever patented in the United States?

426. What common plastic product do we owe to Nathaniel C. Wyeth—son of artist N.C. Wyeth, brother of artists Andrew, Carolyn and Henriette Wyeth, and uncle of artist Jamie Wyeth?

418. $75.

419. The Model N—which sold for $500 in 1906.

420. Melitta Bentz, in Germany in 1908. To improve the quality of coffee for her family, she pierced holes in a tin container, put a circular piece of absorbent paper in the bottom of it and put her creation over a coffee pot.

421. Insecticides. The aerosol dispenser was developed and patented by American chemist Lyle D. Goodhue in 1941.

422. A "toy pistol that blows soap bubbles," which he coinvented with three friends. They designed it in Dos Passos's kitchen for his daughter, Lucy, when she was six years old.

423. Uniforms for the French army. Rioting tailors— fearing they'd be put out of work—broke into the factory and destroyed the machines.

424. Every 200 miles.

425. Thomas Jefferson. The bed was hoisted and secured to the ceiling when it wasn't in use.

426. The now-ubiquitous plastic soda bottle. He developed it as an engineer for the DuPont Company.